"TEEN-AGER"
IS NOT A DISEASE

BY CHARLES M. SCHULZ

Creator of "Peanuts"
and "Young Pillars"

"You know what I think we should have? I think
we should have a Humane Society for teen-agers!"

WARNER PRESS • ANDERSON, INDIANA

"I used to be able to memorize scripture, but you know how it is as you get older. . . . Your mind just doesn't work as well!"

" 'The minutes of the last meeting were read and accepted.' Isn't that wonderful? That sort of gets me right here!"

"I want all of you to direct your attention to this brick. . . . If we can somehow get hold of only seven hundred and fifty thousand more like it, we can build our new church!"

"I'm in charge of the paper-sale for Youth Fellowship this month, Dad. . . . Do you think we could start subscribing to a paper?"

"Well, then, let's put it this way. . . . Suppose that, instead of an apple, Eve had offered him a shiny sports car?"

"OVERDUE? How could this book be overdue when I've only read the first two chapters?"

"Could you hold the line for just a moment? I think I'm about to be hit on the head with my own shoe!"

"Step right in. . . . I'll hold the door for you!"

"Why don't the rest of you go ahead with your games?
I'll call you when the wieners are ready."

"Then again what happens if the world comes to an end before I grow up, and get a chance to become a minister, and warn everybody about the world coming to an end?"

"I hope you won't be offended, Gladys, but did you know that one of the reasons I first fell for you was that you have a face like a great big pizza?"

"What's the matter? Don't you like ice cream cones?"

"Do you want to meet me after school but before Hi-Y, or after Hi-Y but before Student Council, or after Student Council but before Youth Fellowship?"

"You are my Dad. . . . I am your son. . . . Isn't that a thrilling thought? How about letting me use the car to-night?"

"I wonder if there's such a thing as a spiritual dentist?
I think my whole personality is full of cavities!"

" 'In the beginning God created the heaven and the earth.' . . . How's that for being able to quote scripture?"

"House-to-house visitation, my eye! You stay away from Gloria!"

". . . And then after that we'll go to some fancy restaurant for supper unless of course you'd rather we'd just spend the whole evening at your house. . . . Hint, hint, hint, hint!"

"Two dollars and forty-five cents? Wow! I had no idea
I was paying for the feast of Belshazzar!"

"Right after the morning service our whole group is going skin-diving!"

"And then I thought I'd conclude with an illustration of how important it is not to hide your light under a bushel!"

"I must be getting better. . . . They're all in the target!"

"I'm proud to be able to say that I've never been late for a Sunday morning service. . . . Would you care for a piece of toast?"

"It started out be a Ping-Pong table for the Youth group, but somehow along the line it turned into a coffee table for the Woman's Missionary Society!"

"I nominate Fred for program chairman because he's a young man with ideas and lots of drive and because we all know that nobody else will take the job!"

"Congratulations, Mom. . . . You're the only mother I know who has a son who has studied his Sunday school lessons for seven years in advance!"

"So who else do you know who has an electric guitar he can plug into the lighter in his car?"

"Do you think anyone is interested in the number of hot-dishes the church has served since the day of Pentecost?"

"I'm sure I'd be irresistible to him if I could ever find a perfume that smelled like new tires!"

"We represent the young people of the church, and we've come to you because you're a minister and you know all about everything!"

"I never can remember. . . . Are we uniting FOR something or AGAINST something?"

"I think I'm beginning to understand you better. . . . I've been reading a book called, 'How To Know Your Teen-Ager.'"

"Privacy for making phone calls? Are you kidding?
Around here I have to make my own privacy!"

"So how do I know why he ate locusts? Maybe there weren't any drive-ins around!"

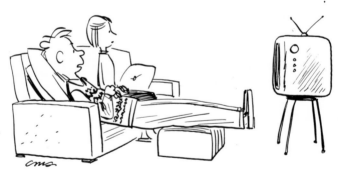

"I wonder what Luke would have recommended for the relief of the pain of headache?"

"Sure, I can listen to the radio, watch TV, read a book, and talk on the telephone all at the same time, but I will admit that I'm glad breathing is automatic!"

"Someday when I get to be rich and famous, I wonder if I'll still be the same sweet, lovable, humble person I am now."

"I enjoyed your sermon on young people, Reverend Hartman. . . . I almost got the impression that you were human once yourself!"

"I realize that we all have to do our part in these Youth Fellowship parties, but there's something humiliating about being put in charge of bringing the toothpicks!"

"I have to hang up now, Gloria. My dad is ready to give me another driving lesson!"

"I like you, Mildred, because you're the kind of girl a guy can talk to. . . . Mildred? Mildred?"

"So she's a little tall. . . . Be proud of her. . . . It's not every guy who can date a girl who played Goliath in a Sunday school pageant!"

"You can tell your dad that his world globe is defective.
. . . It doesn't have on it the town where I was born."

"If we won't have mothers and fathers up in heaven, Mom, what do you think you'd like to have me call you?"

"I wish ol' King Herod had been here, Brother Forbes.
. . . You would have had him all shook up!"

"I have been told that to make a boy like you, you have to learn to talk about the subject he is most interested in. . . . Do you have any books on eating?"

"I just signed up for my fourth straight year at youth camp. . . . I mean . . . wow . . . how spiritual can you get?"

"I'm a teen-ager and you're a teen-ager. . . . Isn't it wonderful to have so much in common?"

"It's not just you, Harriet, honestly. . . . I'm going to give up ALL girls until I find out what's wrong with my Ping Pong!"

"I'm sorry; I should have warned you. . . . Never hold our family Bible upside down!"

"I rolled down the sleeves of my sweatshirt because I think it's nice to be dressed up once in a while!"

"Sure, my ears are freezing, but if I put on earmuffs, no one will be able to see my beautiful sideburns!"

"Let's face it, sir. . . . What I'm really looking for is a list of good scriptures to memorize in case I get into a violent religious argument and need something to say!"

"If this paper misspells the name of our church just once more, I'm going to write a letter to the editor and accuse him of religious bigotry!"

"What do you mean, I'm not as spiritual as I could be? I bowl in **three** church leagues, don't I?"

"I think I must be making progress. . . . Three times this week I've been accused of being a religious fanatic!"

"I used to consider myself an authority on the Book of Revelation, but one day I came across somebody who had read it!"

"My girl and I have a religious problem, Mom. She says, 'Ah-men' and I say, 'Ay-men.' . . . Do you think we have a chance to find happiness together?"

"Waitress, would you mind if I took these watermelon rinds home with me? I have a grandmother who likes to make pickles."

"I think I've made one of the first steps toward unraveling the mysteries of the Old Testament. . . . I'm starting to read it!"

"No, I think anyone who wears hamburger buns for earmuffs should expect to be followed by little dogs!"

"So how can I kneel in front of my bed to say my prayers?
I sleep in the upper bunk!"

"Did you ever have a dream that really shook you up, Mom? Last night I dreamed that Albert Schweitzer was beating me over the head with a Sunday school quarterly!"